MENTOU-SALON.

papa · maman · alienor · dorothee · lydia

OLIVER PRESTON.

Wishing You a Very Happy New Year
MM.X.II
Amicalement

love

Pierre and Silvia

6/19
Humor 5

ANOTHER LOG ON THE FIRE

ANOTHER LOG ON THE FIRE

OLIVER PRESTON.

BEVERSTON PRESS

For Francine and Michelle

First published in Great Britain in 2011 by

BEVERSTON PRESS

Tetbury, Glos GL8 8TT

British Library cataloguing in Publication Data
A catalogue record for this title is available from The British Library

ISBN 978 0 9549936 3 4

Designed by boinggraphics.co.uk
Printed by Gutenberg Press, Malta

OLIVER PRESTON

INTRODUCTION

'While old testament prophets thundered and Drake sailed around the world, Preston sat, looking out of the window, with no visible quickening of the pulse'. This family school report from an eminent history teacher rather aptly summarises those moments that I am required to produce a cartoon 'on tap'. For, like the old Martini advertisement, *any time, any place, anywhere',* ideas seem to come randomly, generated by hearsay or at the most unlikely of moments, and these have to be scribbled on scraps, on sketchpads, the back of envelopes, even receipts, for use at a future date. One such cartoon is *This Way Up* (left). It became the working title of this new collection of my cartoons, the sequel to *Shall we join the Men?* On the reverse of the book, would have been written, *The Other Way Up,* but I am afraid, on reflection, coffins on covers do not sell books, and the title was discarded.

The drawing for the cover of *Another Log on the Fire* is however a firm favourite of mine; it depicts cold winter evenings in England that demand roaring open fires with a regular top up of logs, and the cartoon aims to mimic that peculiarly english trait of survival in large, stately country houses, with a bare minimum of central heating, but a little help from hot water bottles, electric heaters and a few extra layers of clothing. George Sprod, the Punch cartoonist, summarised it perfectly with his drawing of the new guest in the spare bedroom*: 'It's a little chilly, so I've put an extra dog on the bed.' Many of these drawings were first reproduced in *The Field Magazine* which have published my cartoons for over fifteen years. I aim to observe life outside of London, the vagaries of country life, the importance of dogs and of course there is a strong influence from my young family here at home in the Cotswolds.

Most weeks I visit London, staying at the fabulous Chelsea Arts Club, and see clients or visit The Cartoon Museum in Bloomsbury. The museum is an eclectic repository of some of Britain's finest cartoons, a quirky space where exhibitions are held of my heroes - H.M.Bateman, William Heath Robinson, Thelwell, Ronald Searle and the feisty political cartoonists that are preeminent in Britain today. The museum opened its doors in 2006 and over 30,000 visitors now flock annually to immerse themselves in this museum of laughter.

Nothing gives me more pleasure when in a card shop, or standing on our stand at the Game Fair, or at one of my exhibitions, to hear giggles, or sometimes a cacophany of cackles and laughter as people get one of my jokes, and show it to one of their friends. Aristotle said that, 'the secret to good humour is surprise', and I think a test for a good cartoon is one where you can hide the caption but see the drawing - and it tells you nothing. Hide the drawing and read the caption, it still tells you nothing. But put the two together and you are presented with the ensemble of the joke, a cartoon that should be well drawn and get its message across in a few seconds.

If I have achieved this with but a few of the cartoons in these pages then I will be a happy man.

*The Punch Cartoon Album, 150 years of Classic Cartoons, 1990. George Sprod. P.108

OLIVER PRESTON.

'Well, we can't afford to send them ALL to Eton'

'That WAS the single. Would you like the price of a return?'

'Which one of you FOOLS asked him about the weather?'

'I see the Hunt has been through this morning.'

'You've got to be joking.'

'Seeing as it's a special occasion, I thought I'd look after the kids.'

'Are you going to tell him, or shall I?'

'I shouldn't tell your mother. She'll hit the roof."'

'Hey guys, they've changed the sheets!'

'I told you we had a mole.'

'We've just fired the last gardener. He left the estate immediately.'

'It's home rules I'm afraid.'

'Great news, darling. Someone's taken the cottage.'

'It's the only way we can afford the school fees.'

'I'm going to have to hurry you. It won't be on the market for long.'

'Mummy, everyone's gone. Now can we get back in our own car?'

'Mummy I've opened all your presents... They're rubbish.'

'What anniversary?!'

'We'd like to UP our insurance. The grandchildren are coming to stay.'

'For 500 years the family supported the king. Now they support Chelsea.'

'Darling, it's so nice to be celebrating your 39th birthday yet again.'

'Is ANYONE listening to my story?'

'I don't think you've met. They're terribly horsey.'

'I know you're in there.'

'Okay I lost my service. Spare us the amateur dramatics.'

'Did you keep the receipt?'

'You look a million dollars. Is that how much it cost?'

*'Would you like to know
what they would have been worth as a pair?'*

'You know your banker in the Derby? It went bust.'

OLIVER PRESTON

'We've forgotten our corkscrew. Can we borrow your butler?'

'They're always ready when we're away on holiday,
so this year we thought we'd take them with us.'

'I don't care what your SATNAV says. Those are my lettuces.'

'Would it help if I took my feet out of the stirrups?'

OLIVER PRESTON

'She doesn't turn RIGHT on planes.'

'Do I look as though I need a work permit?'

'I still wish we'd gone fishing in Scotland.'

'No, no, quite wrong. NOT fishing on the Test.
My husband was bidding on a week in Barbados.'

'Ladies, LADIES, please! It's ONLY a game of Bridge.'

'...23 brace, a blackberry and an iphone...'

'There's nobody here at the moment. John's shooting grouse, and I'm in St. Tropez with the children. Please leave a message after the tone.'

'Your dog's picked up some bad habits this summer.'

'It's the only way of getting the guns out again after lunch.'

'Daddy, it's a BOYS shoot.'

'If it's that important to you, why don't you get it yourself?'

'My plants are committing suicide.'

'So we said, "Stuff the garden. Let's have a drink instead."'

'Surprise!'

'Ignore the dogs. They beg.'

'Hey guys, this one's from London.'

OLIVER PRESTON

'Do you remember central heating?
That little button you press and everything warms up?'

'I thought you said you knew lots of single men.'

*'On the bright side, the redundancy at the nursery
has rekindled Stewart's interest in golf.'*

'Just hand me the letter, Miss. Pegthorpe.'

'My father was a fishmonger.'

'It was either him or us.'

'No, let me. You did lunch.'

'Let's pretend. You're George Clooney and we're the Sugarbabes.'

'Do you remember when we used to get really good christmas presents?'

'You can come out of the potting shed. They've gone.'

"Madam, he's a fine bird. See how he looks at you straight in the eye.'

ACKNOWLEDGEMENTS

Illustration Acknowledgements

9,10,11,12,15,17,21,25,27,28,29,31,32,33,35,37,39,41,43,45,46,47,49,52,53,55,57,59,60,61,63, 65,66,67,69,71,72,73,75,77,78,79,81,83,85,87,88,89,91,93,95 *The Field Magazine*, 2005-20011.

5 *The Independent.*
34 *The Resident.*
40,82 *The Racing Magazine.*
40 *The Polo Magazine.*
16, 30 *First Eleven Magazine.*

By the same author

Liquid Limericks (2001)	Robson Books	with Alistair Sampson
Larder Limericks (2004)	Robson Books	with Alistair Sampson
Shall we join the Men (2005)	Beverston Press	
Modern Cautionary Verses (2006)	Constable Robinson	with Charlie Ottley
Hitting the Slopes (2008)	Beverston Press	
How to be Asked Again (2009)	Quiller	with Rosie Nickerson
Out of Town (2010)	Beverston Press	
Out for a Duck (2010)	Quiller	with Ian Valentine
Fondue and Furs (2011)	Beverston Press	
Real Men Drink Port (2011)	Quiller	with Ben Howkins

My thanks to Simon Russell at Boing for the design and layout preparation, and Bobby Blackstock at The Gutenberg Press, Malta, for printing and advice. Thank you to Jill Schumm at Beverston Press, and Jonathan Young, editor, and Rebecca Hawtrey Art Editor at *The Field Magazine*, Richenda Hines, editor *The Polo Magazine* and *The Racing Magazine*, and Annabel Butler, editor, *First Eleven Magazine*. To Nick and Elsbeth Preston, Vivien, Amber and Rex, and Otto, for such a wonderful source of ideas.

Prints and greeting cards available from '*Another Log on the Fire*'
Visit www.beverstonpress.com or call +44 (0) 1666 502638